SNOOPY STARS
AS
THE THINKER

Charles M. Schulz

ЯR
RAVETTE BOOKS

First published by
Ravette Books Limited 1989

Printed and bound in Great Britain
for Ravette Books Limited,
3 Glenside Estate, Star Road, Partridge Green,
Horsham, West Sussex RH13 8RA
by Cox & Wyman Ltd, Reading

ISBN 1 85304 171 8

FELICITAS EST PARVUS CANIS CALIDUS

THAT'S LATIN FOR "HAPPINESS IS A WARM PUPPY"

I CAN'T STAND IT!

1-11   SCHULZ

"IN THE BOOK OF LIFE, THE ANSWERS ARE NOT IN THE BACK!"

THAT'S MY NEW PHILOSOPHY

I THINK YOU'RE IN TROUBLE

PEANUTS

PSYCHIATRIC HELP 5¢

THE DOCTOR IS [IN]

IT USED TO BE THAT A PERSON COULD LIVE ISOLATED FROM THE WORLD'S PROBLEMS...

THEN IT GOT TO BE THAT WE ALL KNEW EVERYTHING THAT WAS GOING ON...

THE DOCTOR

THE PROBLEM NOW IS THAT WE KNOW EVERYTHING ABOUT EVERYTHING EXCEPT WHAT'S GOING ON

THAT'S WHY YOU FEEL NERVOUS... FIVE CENTS, PLEASE!

I'M SHORT OF A NICKEL, I'M STILL NERVOUS, AND I STILL DON'T KNOW WHAT'S GOING ON!

THE DOCTOR

SCHULZ

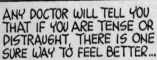

THAT DIDN'T REALLY BOTHER ME...IF YOU EXPECT NOTHING, YOU GET NOTHING...

8-9

SCHULZ

PEANUTS

HALLOWEEN WILL SOON BE HERE..

...ND WHAT AM I DOING? I'M ...TTING IN A PUMPKIN PATCH ...TH THIS STUPID KID WAITING ...OR THE "GREAT PUMPKIN"

WHY?

10-30

THE ONLY CONCLUSION I CAN COME TO IS THAT I REPRESENT A DECLINE IN BEAGLE MENTALITY!

BIG DEAL!

NOW, I'M SUPPOSED TO BE REAL GRATEFUL...

A CRUMB HERE AND A CRUMB THERE...

ALL I EVER GET IS A HALF OF SOMETHING OR A LEFT-OVER...AND THEN I'M SUPPOSED TO BE OVERCOME WITH GRATITUDE

A PIECE OF THIS AND A PIECE OF THAT...JUST CRUMBS! I'M ABOUT TENTH-CLASS!

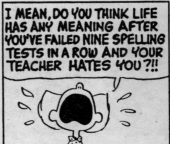

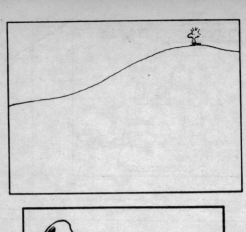

2-13

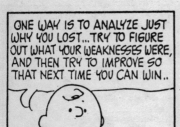

BAM
BAM
BAM
BAM

I RECOGNIZE THAT KICK...THAT'S THE KICK OF SOMEONE WHO HAS AWAKENED IN THE MIDDLE OF THE NIGHT, AND WANTS TO KNOW THE MEANING OF LIFE...

IN THE ENTIRE HISTORY OF THE WORLD, THERE'S NO RECORD OF SANTA CLAUS EVER FILLING THE STOCKING OF A BIRD...

BUT THAT DOESN'T DISCOURAGE WOODSTOCK..

HE FEELS THE ODDS ARE WITH HIM!

© 1979 United Feature Syndicate, Inc.

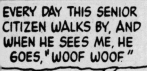

HE SECRET OF LIFE IS TO HANG AROUND PEOPLE WHO DON'T KNOW THE DIFFERENCE!

OR WHATEVER

DON'T STAY HERE...
THEY'LL COME AND GET
YOU WITH A RAKE..

© 1984 United Feature Syndicate, Inc.

NOBODY EVER
TELLS THEM
ABOUT THE
GUY WITH
THE RAKE..

EXPLAIN THIS, IF YOU CAN, CHUCK..EVERYONE IN OUR CLASS HAD TO WRITE AN ESSAY ON WHAT WE DID DURING CHRISTMAS VACATION

WHEN I GOT MINE BACK, THE TEACHER HAD GIVEN ME A "D MINUS".. WELL, I'M USED TO THAT, RIGHT, CHUCK? RIGHT!

NOW, GUESS WHAT..ALL THOSE ESSAYS WENT INTO A CITY ESSAY CONTEST, AND I WON! EXPLAIN THAT, CHUCK

1-9-85

NEVER LISTEN TO THE REVIEWERS

© 1984 United Feature Syndicate, Inc.

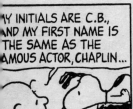

I COULDN'T DECIDE IF I WANTED MARBLE FUDGE, CHOCOLATE, ROCKY ROAD, VANILLA OR BUTTER PECAN..

FINALLY DECIDED TO [T]RY MARBLE FUDGE.. [T]HEN I HAD TO CHOOSE [B]ETWEEN A PLAIN CONE [O]R A SUGAR CONE...

© 1987 United Feature Syndicate, Inc.

7-3

I DECIDED ON THE SUGAR CONE...SO WHAT HAPPENED? I WENT OUT THE DOOR, AND DROPPED THE WHOLE THING ON THE SIDEWALK!

DON'T TELL ME MY LIFE ISN'T A SHAKESPEAREAN TRAGEDY..

I WON'T

THAT'S STRANGE..I FEEL LIKE I'VE SEEN THAT DOG BEFORE..

1-12

© 1988 United Feature Syndicate, Inc.

ISN'T THERE AN EXPRESSION FOR THAT

DÉJÀ BEAGLE!

E EARS HEAR THE
CAN OPENER..

GHT AWAY THE
OMACH KNOWS THAT
PPER IS COMING..

HOW DO THE EARS
TELL THE STOMACH?

I'VE NEVER BEEN
ABLE TO FIGURE
THAT OUT..

5-17

SOMETIMES, IF YOU PURPOSELY LOOK SAD, THEY'LL BRING YOU AN EXTRA BIG SUPPER...

HI, I NOTICED YOU APPEARED A BIT PEAKED..

I FIGURED YOU PROBABLY WEREN'T FEELING SO GOOD SO I DIDN'T GIVE YOU AS MUCH TO EAT..

7-1

AND SOMETIMES YOU DO SOMETHING THAT IS SO STUPID IT STAGGERS THE IMAGINATION!

Other Snoopy titles published by Ravette Books

Snoopy Stars in this series

No. 1	Snoopy Stars as The Flying Ace	£1.95
No. 2	Snoopy Stars as The Matchmaker	£1.95
No. 3	Snoopy Stars as The Terror of the Ice	£1.95
No. 4	Snoopy Stars as The Legal Beagle	£1.95
No. 5	Snoopy Stars as The Fearless Leader	£1.95
No. 6	Snoopy Stars as Man's Best Friend	£1.95
No. 7	Snoopy Stars as The Sportsman	£1.95
No. 8	Snoopy Stars as The Scourge of The Fairways	£1.95
No. 9	Snoopy Stars as The Branch Manager	£1.95
No. 10	Snoopy Stars as The Literary Ace	£1.95
No. 11	Snoopy Stars as The Great Pretender	£1.95
No. 12	Snoopy Stars as The Dog-Dish Gourmet	£1.95
No. 13	Snoopy Stars as The Fitness Freak	£1.95
No. 14	Snoopy Stars in The Pursuit of Pleasure	£1.95
No. 15	Snoopy Stars as The Weatherman	£1.95
No. 17	Snoopy Stars in The Mixed Doubles	£1.95
No. 18	Snoopy Stars in Brotherly Love	£1.95

Colour landscapes

First Serve	£2.95
Be Prepared	£2.95
Stay Cool	£2.95
Shall We Dance?	£2.95
Let's Go	£2.95
Come Fly With Me	£2.95
Are Magic	£2.95
Hit The Headlines	£2.95

Weekenders

No. 1 Weekender	£4.95

Peanuts at School	£6.95

Black and white landscapes

It's a Dog's Life	£2.50
Roundup	£2.50
Freewheelin'	£2.50
Joe Cool	£2.50
Chariots For Hire	£2.50
Dogs Don't Eat Dessert	£2.50
You're on the Wrong Foot Again, Charlie Brown	£2.50
By Supper Possessed	£2.95
Talk is Cheep, Charlie Brown	£2.95

All these books are available at your local bookshop or news agent, or can be ordered direct from the publisher. Just tick the titles you require and fill in the form below. Prices and availability subject to change without notice.

Ravette Books Limited, 3 Glenside Estate, Star Road, Partridge Green, Horsham, West Sussex RH13 8RA

Please send a cheque or postal order, and allow the following for postage and packing. UK: Pocket-books – 45p for one book 20p for a second book and 15p for each additional book. Other titles – 50p for one book and 30p for each additional book.

Name ....

Address ....

....